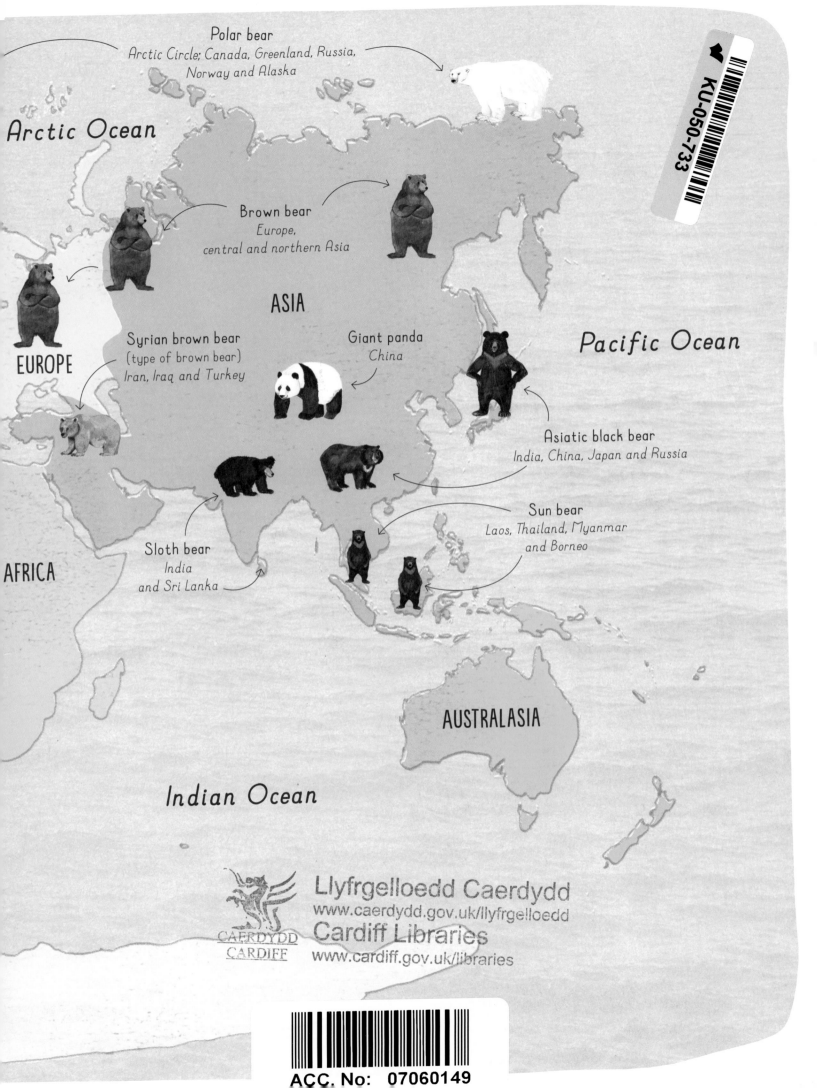

Polar bear
Arctic Circle; Canada, Greenland, Russia, Norway and Alaska

Arctic Ocean

Brown bear
Europe, central and northern Asia

ASIA

EUROPE

Syrian brown bear
(type of brown bear)
Iran, Iraq and Turkey

Giant panda
China

Pacific Ocean

Asiatic black bear
India, China, Japan and Russia

AFRICA

Sloth bear
India and Sri Lanka

Sun bear
Laos, Thailand, Myanmar and Borneo

AUSTRALASIA

Indian Ocean

Spectacled bear

Polar bear

Asiatic black bear
(I live in Asia)

Sun bear

American black bears
Ursus americanus

American black bears live in North America. With a population of around 850,000, they are the most common species of bear on the planet.

There are at least 16 different subspecies of American black bear. Most are black in colour, like this one...

...but others are not black at all. Like these:

GLACIER BEAR
Ursus americanus emmonsii
Sometimes called the blue bear because of their grey or silvery-blue fur, these bears are extremely rare and only live in Alaska.

KERMODE BEAR
Ursus americanus kermodei
Kermode bears look like small polar bears, but they are actually a rare, creamy-coloured subspecies of American black bear. Sometimes called spirit bears, they live in British Columbia, Canada.

This could be a good spot for a long nap!

HOW DO THEY SIZE UP?

American black bears can reach 2 metres tall and weigh more than 250 kilograms. They are the third biggest species of bear, coming in behind the polar bear and the brown bear.

ADULT FEMALE (SOW)   ADULT MALE (BOAR)

CUB

3m

2m

1m

Most American black bears go into a deep kind of sleep for long stretches of time over winter. This is called hibernation. They make dens in caves, burrows and other sheltered spots, using leaves to make them comfy and cosy.

American black bears usually eat grasses, fruit and nuts, but they will eat most things that they can get their paws on.

Bears living on national parks have learnt that campsites are a good place to find food. They are often spotted helping themselves to snacks if they can find them.

PLEASE DO
NOT FEED
THE BEARS

Brown bears
Ursus arctos

There are about 200,000 brown bears living across the world. They are widespread, with populations in North America, northern Europe and northern Asia.

There are around 15 different subspecies of brown bear. They vary in size and their colours range from very light brown to almost black. Here are a few of them.

MAINLAND GRIZZLY BEAR
Ursus arctos horribilis
The word grizzly means 'tipped with grey'. These bears get their name from the grey specks found all over their fur. They live in North America.

SYRIAN BROWN BEAR
Ursus arctos syriacus
These bears tend to be quite light in colour and they are one of the smaller brown bear subspecies. They live in the Middle East.

KODIAK BEAR
Ursus arctos middendorffi
These are the largest of the brown bears. They live on Kodiak Island in Alaska and are sometimes called the Alaskan brown bear.

Brown bears have a large hump of pure muscle over their shoulders. This makes them very strong indeed.

HOW DO THEY SIZE UP?

Kodiak bears can grow up to 3 metres tall and weigh up to 680 kilograms. That's as heavy as six adult giant pandas! Very close in size to the polar bear, this subspecies of brown bear is huge!

ADULT MALE (BOAR)
ADULT FEMALE (SOW)
CUB
3m
2m
1m

Known for their love of salmon, brown bears can eat 30 of these tasty fish in just one day. Often, they only eat the heads.

...but a few of us like to use more modern methods, like fishing rods and nets!

Most brown bears like to fish using their mouths and their sharp claws...

Asiatic black bears *Ursus thibetanus*

Asiatic black bears live across eastern, southern and Southeast Asia, in countries including India, China, Japan and Russia. There are around 60,000 Asiatic black bears living in the wild.

Very good at climbing, Asiatic black bears spend a lot of their time up in the trees searching for nuts, fruit, insects and honey.

Asiatic black bears have a thick bushy mane and big round ears.

Their chins are often white and their snouts are a lighter colour than their bodies.

Some people call Asiatic black bears 'moon bears' because they have a moon-shaped marking on their chests.

Asiatic black bears have incredible upper body strength. Their front legs are so strong that they can climb trees almost without using their back legs at all.

HOW DO THEY SIZE UP?

Asiatic black bears are normally less than 2 metres tall. Adults can weigh up to 200 kilograms. That's heavy, but it's only about a third of the weight of a large brown bear!

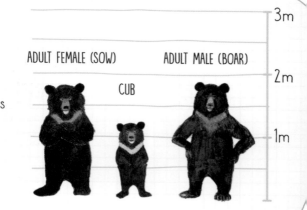

ADULT FEMALE (SOW)   ADULT MALE (BOAR)

CUB

3m

2m

1m

Asiatic black bears are great at standing upright and walking on two legs. This special skill is called being 'bipedal'. It can be useful for bears when reaching high-up food or exploring their surroundings.

We like to keep strong with a little bit of weightlifting.

Sun bears
Helarctos malayanus

There are fewer than 10,000 sun bears in the world, and they live in the tropical rainforests of Southeast Asia.

Sun bears have short fur so that they can stay cool in hot weather and they have long, curved claws that are perfect for sticking into tight spots to reach honey and other tasty food.

Their super-long tongues help them to extract honey from beehives. This special skill, and their love of honey, has given them the nickname of the honey bear.

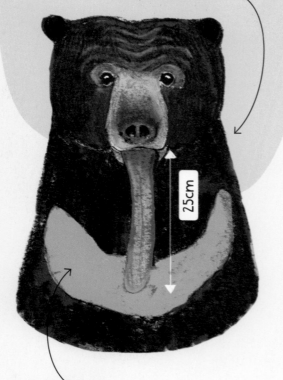

25cm

Sun bears get their more common name from the sun-shaped, yellow marking on their chests.

HOW DO THEY SIZE UP?

At around 1.4 metres tall, sun bears are the world's smallest species of bear. They weigh up to 80 kilograms. That's less than half as heavy as an American black bear.

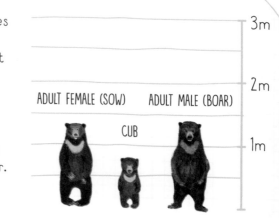

3m

2m

ADULT FEMALE (SOW)   ADULT MALE (BOAR)

CUB

1m

Sun bears are a shy species of bear and they like to spend their time hidden away in trees eating honey.

Their small size (which is great for climbing) and their long tongues mean they're perfectly suited for this pastime.

Sloth bears
Melursus ursinus

There are about 20,000 sloth bears in the world today. They live in the forests and grasslands of India and Sri Lanka, in southern Asia. Baloo in *The Jungle Book* is a sloth bear.

THE FEMALE SLOTH BEAR IS THE ONLY BEAR THAT GIVES HER BABIES A RIDE

Once a sloth bear has used its claws to rip a hole in a termite mound, it puts its lips over the spot and noisily sucks up as many termites as it can – slurp! These clever bears can even shut their nostrils to stop the insects crawling up their noses.

SUPER-LONG, CURVED CLAWS FOR BREAKING INTO TERMITE MOUNDS AND BEEHIVES

But the most important thing to remember is...

...SLOTH BEARS ARE NOT SLOTHS!

They just share the same name. 'Sloth' means laziness, but these bears work hard to get enough termites to eat.

FREE TERMITES WHILE YOU WAIT!

Sloth bears love to eat ants and tiny insects called termites, which live inside hard mounds of earth. They can eat thousands of termites in one day.

HOW DO THEY SIZE UP?

Sloth bears can grow up to 1.8 metres tall and adult bears weigh up to 140 kilograms. They are the second smallest bear species.

ADULT FEMALE (SOW)   CUB   ADULT MALE (BOAR)

3m
2m
1m

SALLY'S SLOTH BEAR SALON

Sloth bears have long, shaggy fur coats and they can look a bit messy. They have thick black hair around their faces, which forms a kind of mane, and they can get very dusty while they're busy hoovering up insects in the dirt.

That's why some of us pop to the salon for a spot of grooming and a trim.

Giant pandas
Ailuropoda melanoleuca

Giant pandas are bears too! They live in cold, wet bamboo forests in the mountains of central China. Today there are probably fewer than 2,000 left in the wild. They are the rarest of all the bears.

Their famous black and white fur makes giant pandas easy to recognize.

There is a subspecies of the giant panda called the Qinling panda. It is smaller than the giant panda and it has brown and white fur, rather than black and white.

The red panda and the giant panda both have a big appetite for bamboo, but they do not belong to the same family. The red panda is more closely related to raccoons than to bears.

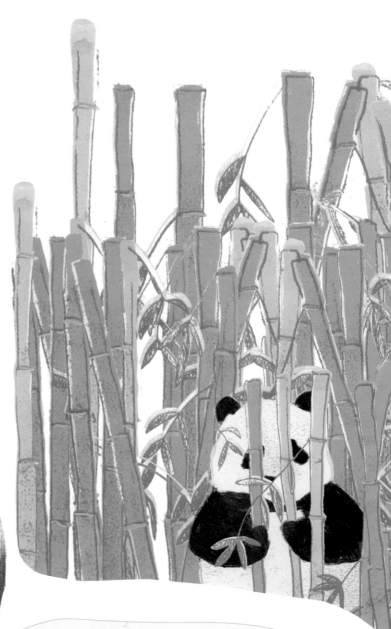

HOW DO THEY SIZE UP?

One of the smaller bear species, giant pandas grow to around 1.8 metres. A big male can weigh more than 120 kilograms, about half the weight of a big American black bear.

ADULT MALE (BOAR)

ADULT FEMALE (SOW)

CUB

3m

2m

1m

Giant pandas love to eat bamboo. They live in thick bamboo forests so that they can be surrounded by their favourite food.

At least 12 hours of a giant panda's day are spent chewing on bamboo stems.

We like to do other things too, like playing hide-and-seek!

Spectacled bears

Tremarctos ornatus

Spectacled bears are the only bears that are native to South America. There are fewer than 20,000 of these bears in the wild.

They mainly live in the Andes Mountains, which is why they are often known as the Andean bear.

The spectacled bear is the only short-faced bear living today. The other seven species of bear have longer noses.

THEIR SNOUT IS QUITE FLAT

Between 500,000 and 2 million years ago, an ancestor of today's spectacled bear roamed the planet. The giant short-faced bear (*Arctotherium angustidens*) stood at a whopping 3.3 metres tall!

CAN YOU NAME A FAMOUS BEAR FROM SOUTH AMERICA?

Wanted on Voyage

FRAGILE

Spectacled bears get their name from the spectacle-shaped marking around their eyes.

HOW DO THEY SIZE UP?

Spectacled bears can reach 2 metres in height. Adult males weigh up to 200 kilograms, which is roughly twice as heavy as the females.

ADULT FEMALE (SOW)   ADULT MALE (BOAR)

CUB

3m

2m

1m

Polar bears
Ursus maritimus

Polar bears live in the Arctic, a cold, icy place that surrounds the North Pole. There are around 20,000 polar bears in the wild and they are mostly found in parts of Canada, Greenland, Russia, Norway and Alaska in the USA.

Polar bears are amazingly well adapted to their chilly surroundings.

Thick white fur for staying warm and for blending in with their snowy environment. This helps the bears get close to their prey without being seen.

Incredible sense of smell for tracking prey over long distances.

Very large feet (up to 30 centimetres wide!) for walking on snow and ice, and for speedy swimming. Their feet even have fur on the bottom to keep out the cold and their paw pads are covered in small bumps to give them extra grip.

Underneath their fur, polar bears actually have black skin. This absorbs sunlight and keeps them feeling warm and cosy.

Polar bears love to eat seals and, unfortunately for the seals, they are very good at catching them. The bears wait by the edge of the water, or above holes in the ice, and then pounce when a seal appears.

They are very patient animals and can wait for hours and hours at a time.

HOW DO THEY SIZE UP?

Reaching a great height of over 3 metres and weighing up to 700 kilograms, polar bears are not only the biggest of all of the bear species, but they're also the largest meat-eating animal on land. An adult male polar bear can weigh up to ten times as much as a sun bear!

ADULT FEMALE (SOW)

ADULT MALE (BOAR)

CUB

3m

2m

1m

You could try
searching for seals
with a snorkel.

Polar bears are great at sneaking
up on their prey. Their long necks
also give them a good view above
the water while they swim.

Eating

One thing that all bears have in common is their love of food.

Bears find food in all sorts of places and what they eat depends on where they live, what time of year it is and what they can get their paws on. But most bears have a favourite dish…

Brown bears are particularly fond of salmon and berries. But not necessarily at the same time.

Sun bears prefer all things honey-flavoured, including honeycomb, bees and, best of all, honey itself.

Sloth bears like a range of different foods, including fruit, insects and eggs, but their real favourite is lots and lots of termites.

Panda bears just love bamboo – they can eat for hours on end and they never get bored of it.

American black
bears like to eat
grasses, berries
and nuts.

Polar bears have
a taste for seals.
Don't tell the seals!

Spectacled bears
love wild fruit and
nuts. In zoos, they
are especially keen
on oranges.

Asiatic black
bears also like
fruit, and a side
plate of insects
is always a
bonus!

Swimming

All eight species of bear are good swimmers. Some swim to catch food, some swim to travel from place to place and some swim just for the fun of it!

However, some are much fonder of a splash than others.

Polar bears are the best swimmers of all the bears. All-rounders when it comes to life in the water, they can swim for an amazing 350 kilometres without stopping, dive deep down into the ocean and even jump out of the water to catch seals that are lying on the ice.

Even though giant pandas can swim, they don't enjoy it as much as the other bears do. Eating almost nothing but bamboo, pandas don't need to find food in the water and they don't need to swim across lakes or rivers to get around, so swimming isn't a big part of their routine.

The American black bear and the sloth bear both enjoy being in the water and are very good swimmers. They like to snack on fish when they can catch them.

The spectacled bear, the sun bear and the Asiatic black bear are strong swimmers, too.

Brown bears love being in the water and are expert swimmers. They spend a lot of time hunting for fish (especially salmon) in rivers, and sometimes they like a dip to relax.

Climbing

All bears have strong legs and sharp claws, but they are not all good climbers. Some bears spend hours high up in the trees, while others struggle to reach the first branch. Cubs are better climbers than their big, heavy parents.

Bears climb for all sorts of reasons, including to find food, to hide from other animals and even to have a rest or a sleep in the treetops.

Giant pandas, especially cubs, have a lot of fun climbing trees.

American black bears are great climbers. They climb to reach tasty food and to hide if they're scared.

Brown bears are often too heavy to climb trees once they are fully grown, but they love to use the trunks for a good old scratch.

Running

Bears don't often run a long way. They usually save running for when they are trying to get away from predators or they want to scare another animal.

But when they do run, some can be extremely fast!

BROWN BEAR

AMERICAN BLACK BEAR

SPECTACLED BEAR

GIANT PANDA

POLAR BEAR

SUN BEAR

ASIATIC BLACK BEAR

SLOTH BEAR

The giant panda and the sloth bear are reluctant runners. They'd usually rather take their time and walk instead!

Over short distances, the brown bear and the American black bear are both super speedy. They can run much faster than a human.

Hibernating

During the winter, some bears hibernate. Hibernation is when animals make a den and go into a deep sleep for the coldest months of the year. They can sleep for months on end and it helps them to save energy while there isn't much food around to eat.

Not all bears hibernate. Sun bears and spectacled bears don't need to hibernate, because they live in warm places. Sloth bears rest in caves during winter, but don't actually hibernate. When it gets cold in the mountains, giant pandas move lower down to where it is a little warmer.

That leaves four hibernating bears...

ASIATIC BLACK BEAR
Not all Asiatic black bears hibernate, but they do if they are pregnant or if they live in especially cold places.

BROWN BEAR
Brown bears often hibernate from October to May.

They tend to dig out dens on slopes, making a small tunnel that leads to a larger space for sleeping in.

AMERICAN BLACK BEAR

Most American black bears hibernate, especially the ones who live in the chillier climates. They dig a den under rocks, in trees or in undergrowth and nestle down until spring.

POLAR BEAR

Only pregnant polar bears hibernate. They reappear once their cubs are a few months old.

They dig out a snow den on a slope. It has an entrance tunnel and a special hole to let in air through the snow, so they can breathe more easily. Even though the den is built out of snow, it can get very warm in there!

The future

Some bears like warm weather, but I much prefer cold snow and ice. I hope it doesn't melt away completely.

I don't know what I would do without bamboo!

Please look after our natural habitats.

Sometimes humans make life difficult for bears. If climate change makes the world too warm, polar bears won't have enough snow and ice for hunting seals and digging winter dens. If we cut down forests to build cities and farms, black bears and brown bears will have nowhere to live. By protecting the places where bears live, we can help make sure they have a safe future.